Shots and Cocktails

Alcopops

Gin and Tonic

Glass of Sherry

These units are based on pub measures. When you pour yourself a whisky or a glass of wine at home, they're usually bigger, so you'd better add 20%!

Are you ready for your drinking diary?

Now that you know about units, it's time to add them up. Drink normally for the next seven days and fill in the diary overleaf with what you drank and the number of units you put away each day.

What I'm Drinking - Honest

	SESSION 1 WHAT I DRANK AND WHERE	SESSION 2 WHAT I DRANK AND WHERE	WH
Example	Two pints at lunchtime 6 Units	Two glasses of wine with dinner 4.6 units	
MON			
TUE			
WED			
THU			
FRI			
SAT			
SUN			

3 D WHERE	TOTAL UNITS NOW	TOTAL UNITS at 8 weeks	TOTAL UNITS at 16 weeks
	10.6		

VERY IMPORTANT COLUMN
We'll explain later

MON	
TUES	
WED	
THUR	
FRI	
SAT	
SUN	

NOW, ABOUT THOSE 2 DAYS

If you're a bit alarmed by the total units in your diary, don't worry. You can cut down easily and permanently with our 2- day method.

Here's how it works:

Look at your drinking diary and choose the day with the smallest number of units. This is the day you're going to make into **No Day.**

That is, the one day in the week that you don't drink alcohol at all. Yes, that's right – just one day!

We're going to help you do it on the next few pages and we promise it will be easier than you think.

Now look at your diary again and choose a second day. It could be one with fewer than average units, or the one that you feel would be easiest to make into **Lo Day.** That is, the day when you drink **half as much** alcohol as you did in your diary.

Again, we'll help you with a method that really works and doesn't hurt!

Easy method coming up...

CHANGE THE WHAT, CHANGE THE WHERE

... and make it easy on yourself

WHAT you drink affects the amount of alcohol you take in.

A shandy is half as alcoholic as a lager. A glass of wine is twice as strong as a spritzer. A glass of Lambrusco is much less alcoholic than a glass of Shiraz. And soft drinks are not alcoholic at all.

So if you change WHAT you drink, you can reduce or eliminate daily units quite easily.

WHERE you drink is the other big thing you can change.

If you drink at home while watching TV, you'll cut down your intake by going out for a walk instead, or to the cinema.

If you drink at the pub, it'll be easy to stop or cut down for a day if you go somewhere else - dance classes, to see a friend, to the library, to a concert… like that.

By thinking about each drinking session in your diary and choosing the change that will be easiest to make - the WHAT or the WHERE - you'll find that fixing your drinking problem really is just a 2-day task.

And don't forget, you can mix and match WHAT and WHERE on the same day. Like Neil.

It's time you met Neil...

Neil's NO daY

Neil changes *The What* and *The Where* on a 2-session day.

Now let's hear from Lisa

13

Lisa's LO daY

NOW IT'S YOUR TURN

Choose your No Day and your Lo Day

Turn back to page **5** and pick your days. Make it easy on yourself and choose days that are already low in units for your

and your

Think about how easy it will be to change the **WHATs** and the **WHEREs** as you make your decision, and when you've settled on your days, mark them in the special column like this:

Now decide on a start date and go for it!

At the end of 8 weeks, you'll be well into your new routine and will be able to fill in the 8-week column in your diary with your new daily units.

You'll have cut your alcohol consumption by around 20% and you ought to be feeling pretty chuffed with yourself!

But what if 20% isn't enough?

YOU DO IT ALL AGAIN IN 8 WEEKS TIME

The 2-day method works over and over

A 20% reduction is a great start, but if you're getting to enjoy having a clear head, you might want to reduce your drinking still further.

No problem. All you need to do is turn back to your diary, choose another **No Day** and another **Lo Day** and follow the whole process again.

Then, 8 weeks later, fill in your new units score in the spare column and give yourself a pat on the back for having fixed your drinking problem with the 2-day method!

And if you want to go on and eliminate alcohol altogether, just switch your **Lo Days** to **No Days**, change the **WHAT** and the **WHERE**, and you'll be on the wagon within a few weeks.

HANG ON!
WHAT IF I SLIP UP?

Don't beat yourself up about it

Nobody's perfect and even when you're cutting down just two days a week, there will probably be times when you weaken and have a crafty glug of something naughty.

The trick is not to think of it as a disaster. OK, you had a drink when you shouldn't have, or went to the pub instead of the park. Big deal.

Fixing your drinking problem is like any other habit change – it takes a few weeks to become part of your routine and there are bound to be hiccups along the way.

So give yourself a smack on the back of the hand and get back to the plan next week, increasing your motivation by reminding yourself **why** you're doing this.

SO WHY ARE YOU DOING THIS?

Whatever your reason, write it down

Take a piece of paper and make a note of why you're cutting down your drinking.

Maybe you want to live longer, to see the grandchildren graduate, to get fitter, to get a job, to keep a job, to lose some weight, to catch up with studies, to rescue a relationship…whatever your reason, write it down.

Now fold that bit of paper and keep it with you. Take it out and look at it whenever you weaken.

Next, go into the bathroom and write on the mirror with lipstick or a wax pencil. Write your reason again, where you'll see it every morning.

Now get some sticky notes and write your reason on half a dozen of them. Stick them all over the house – on the fridge, on the TV, on the bedside table, on your PC screen if you have one.

The more you remind yourself why, the less likely you will be to slip.

LET'S RE-CAP THE 2-DAY METHOD

1 Keep a diary for a week so you know how many units you drink every day

2 Pick the day with least units and make this into **NO daY**

3 Change the **WHAT**s and the **WHERE**s to make it easy

4 Now pick the second lightest day and make this into **LO daY**

5 Change the **WHAT**s and the **WHERE**s to make it easy

6 Pick a start date and keep it up for 8 weeks, by which time your new habits will be ingrained and you will have cut your alcohol intake by about 20%

7 If you want to cut further, choose another **No Day** and another **Lo Day** and do it all again for 8 weeks

8 If you want to stop drinking altogether, just change all remaining **Lo Days** into **No Days**.

9 If you slip, don't beat yourself up, just get back to the plan

10 Write your reason everywhere, and look at it every day

Cheers and Good Luck!

A NOTE FOR VERY HEAVY DRINKERS

If you've been a big drinker for a while, you might feel sick or sweaty or even get the shakes during your **No Day.**

In this case, try two **Lo Days** instead.

If you're still feeling bad, it might be best to talk to your doctor and discuss tactics, or contact your local health service

HELP WITH OTHER PROBLEMS

This little book is one of a series by Dr Chris Williams that helps you deal with the challenges life can throw at you.

There are books for depression, anger management, low self-esteem, worry, post-natal depression and stopping smoking. There's one that can help you fix almost anything, like getting a job, making friends or getting out of debt, and there's even one that helps you lose weight and get fitter.

All the books are backed up by a website

www.livinglifetothefull.com

where you can use free audio and video courses and also connect with other people who have similar problems.

You can also read the little books online at www.fiveareasonline.com